Always be a "Keeper of Dreams"!
With best wishes,
Mary Alice Baumgardner

ALEXANDRA

KEEPER OF DREAMS

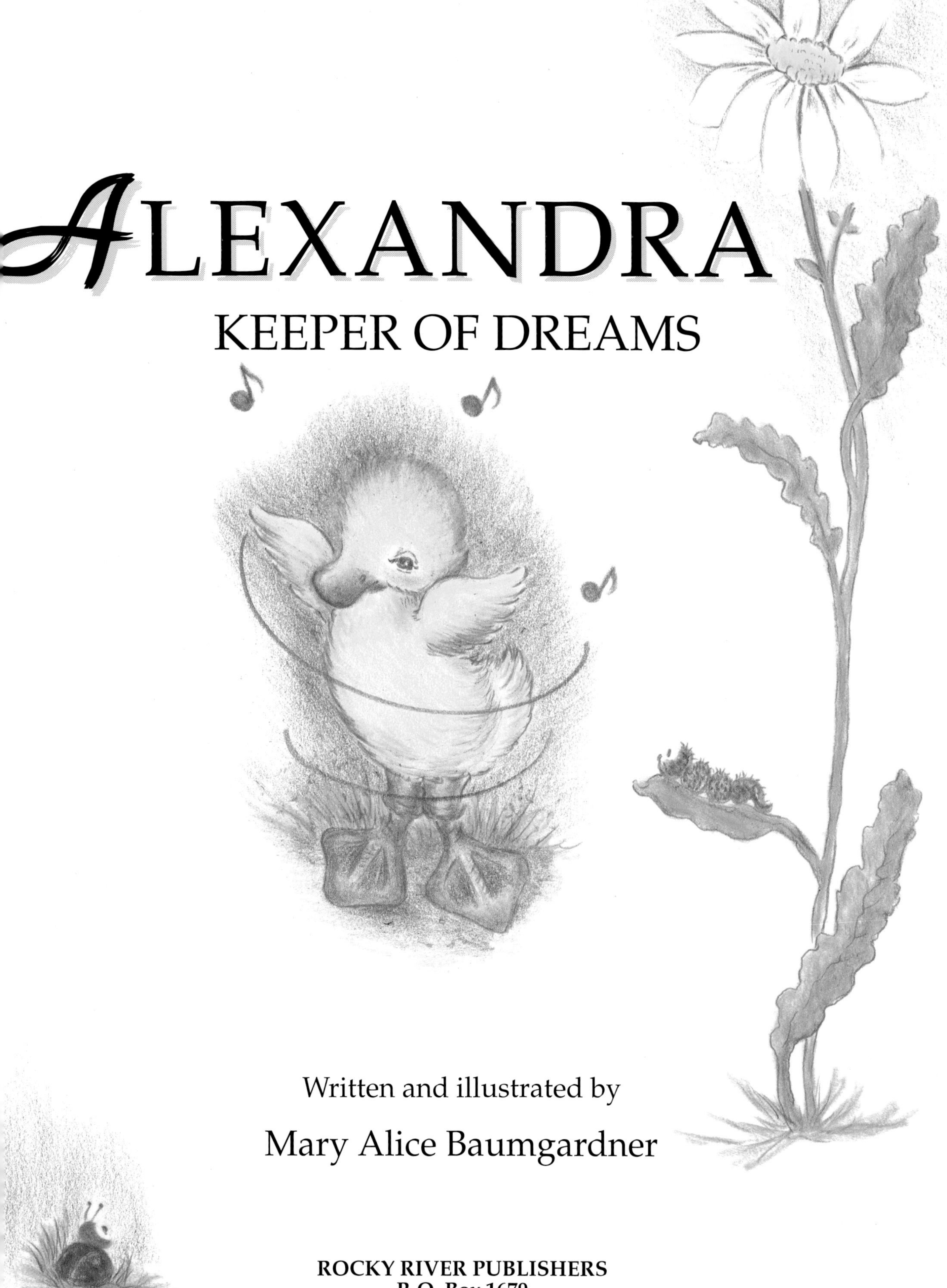

Written and illustrated by

Mary Alice Baumgardner

ROCKY RIVER PUBLISHERS
P. O. Box 1679
Shepherdstown, WV 25443
(304) 876-2711

DEDICATION

This book is dedicated with love and appreciation in memory of my parents, Sarah and George Dress, who always encouraged me to hold on to my dreams.

Editors: Penny Wheeler, Miriam Williams Wilson
Copy Editor: Eugene Lincoln

ISBN 0-944576-08-7
Library of Congress Catalog Card Number: 93-83250

Printing History

First Printing, March 1993

Printed in the United States of America
By WINCHESTER PRINTERS, INC., Winchester, VA 22601
Color separations by GRAPHTEC, 1724 Whitehead Road, Baltimore, MD 21207

Preface for Parents and Teachers

Having special dreams or goals can enhance self-esteem by giving a child a positive focus. It is important from earliest childhood to have dreams respected and nurtured.

As children work to attain their dreams they will gradually grow in an understanding of themselves. They will learn their strengths, abilities, weaknesses, likes, dislikes, limitations, and talents. In the process they will also learn to better understand others. The activities involved in the pursuit of their dreams teach children that much hard work and perseverance are needed to make dreams come true.

Alexandra, a delightful and very determined little duck, had a "preposterous" dream. She worked hard with tremendous determination to achieve her dream. Despite her best efforts her dream seemed impossible to attain. Then one day she made a wonderful discovery ....

Children need to discover that they, too, can become "Keepers of Dreams" like Alexandra Quackendiver. To dream, to strive to accomplish those dreams, and to encourage and nurture the dreams of others will provide children and adults with some of life's greatest joys.

After you have read ALEXANDRA KEEPER OF DREAMS, be sure to read the *Discussion Suggestion Pages* beginning on page 33. You and your child may learn some interesting things about each other!

"Reach high, for stars lie hidden in your soul.
Dream deep, for every dream precedes the goal."

Pamela Naull Starr

Best wishes to you, dear readers, and all those children whose dreams you nurture and lives you touch.

THE ROCKY RIVER FOLKS

Music woke tiny Alexandra Quackendiver. She peeped out from her mother's nest and blinked at the bright colors of a sun-soaked day. Then she stretched and blinked again.

Mama Quackendiver had chosen a wonderful place to build her home not far from the lake in City Park. It was behind tall grass near the stage where outdoor concerts were given.

Alexandra peeked through the tall grass. Her eyes widened as she gazed at the stage. There, whirling about in time to the music, were children …dancing. Alexandra was amazed, for the children's costumes looked just like her feathers!

The music was wonderful. The costumes were beautiful. From that moment on, Alexandra Quackendiver knew she wanted to be a ballet dancer.

“Ducks don’t dance, Alexandra!” Mama quacked. “That is preposterous! Why don’t you practice swimming, like your brothers and sisters?”

“Oh, Mama, this is what I MUST do. Please! Help me,” Alexandra pleaded.

“There has never been a dancing duck,” Mama argued. But she had watched the young dancers many times, so she agreed to help Alexandra learn the ballet positions.

She explained the French ballet words to Alexandra:

to *plié* (plē-ā) is to bend the knees;

to *tour jeté*
(tor-shet-tay)
is to leap and turn
around in the air;

and to *pirouette*
(peer-oo-wet)
is to turn around
on tiptoe.

When the young dancers practiced on stage, Alexandra practiced, too.

She whirled and swirled and twirled in time to the music.

However, she plopped
when she tried to *plié*

She became tangled
trying to *tour jeté*

And her *pirouette* was a sight to forget
as her knees seemed to get in the way.

“It’s my shape, Mama, “ Alexandra complained. I just have too much behind me.”

“I’m so sorry, Dear,” Mama told her, “but you have the shape that has always been in the Quackendiver family. I don’t think you can do anything to change it.”

Alexandra tried to diet.

She tried exercises.

Not eating enough good food made her woozy and weak.

Too much exercise made her feel wobbly.

And still, her shape never changed.

"Why do I dream of being a dancing duck?" Alexandra wondered. "Maybe it is impossible. Yet, it is a dream that somehow seems more real to me than feathers and quacks."

Something inside her kept softly saying, "Alexandra, it is important to hold on to your dreams. Don't quit! You can become a Keeper of Dreams."

And so she kept on trying. She rubbed liniment on her back when her muscles ached.

She put bandages on her knees when they were scraped.

And she listened to beautiful music when her heart was heavy.

One day at lunchtime Alexandra was swimming in the lake for her salad. She dived a little deeper, twisted a little more … and turned in a new direction. And then …

She discovered she now could plié
And complete a grand tour jeté.
Her pirouette *was easier when wet.*
Underwater was great for ballet!

She did a few more glides and turns and twists, then shot to the surface.

"This is marvelous," she quacked before spiraling downward again.

Alexandra's underwater antics caught the attention of Mayfly and Bullfrog. The Brown Trout twins watched in amazement. When she finally finished practicing late that day, the whole lake was abuzz with excitement.

That evening she told Mama and all the little Quackendivers, “My dream has come true. I can do every ballet step I ever tried … only better than I ever hoped. I have a beautiful costume, and the whole lake is my stage!”

From then on Alexandra listened to music, enjoyed salads, and danced underwater everyday. She made many new friends who came to her for dancing lessons. Everyone agreed she should be given a KEEPER OF DREAMS award for holding on to her dream until it came true.

In fact, Alexandra Quackendiver became quite famous … for she had discovered underwater ballet!

The End

ALEXANDRA KEEPER OF DREAMS

DISCUSSION SUGGESTIONS

Dreams help children focus on positive goals. In pursuing their dreams, children can discover their "specialness" and realize that they, too, can make a contribution. We hope these ideas might spark some interesting discussions.

THE ROCKY RIVER FOLKS

"The poor man is not he who is without a cent, but he who is without a dream."

HENRY KEMP

I. **A DREAM is a goal, a challenge, a purpose ... something to reach for.** Usually it takes a long time and hard work to make a dream come true. This isn't the kind of dream we have while sleeping.

A. Do you have a dream?

1. What subjects or activities do you enjoy most?
2. Do you like being alone or with others?
3. What would you do if you could do anything you wanted?

Perhaps the answers to these questions will help you discover your dream.
Your dream is special because there is only one person in the whole world like you!

B. You might not yet know what your dream will be, but be ready to discover it. Perhaps you are good at art, music, or sports. Maybe you are good at helping others, solving mysteries, or seeing a need and doing something about it. When you feel strongly about doing something that might make you a better person ... or the world a better place – that just might be your dream!

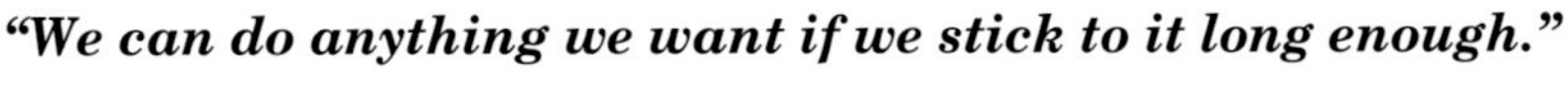
"We can do anything we want if we stick to it long enough."

HELEN KELLER

II. **A KEEPER OF DREAMS holds on to hope.** He or she obeys that something inside that says, "Hold on to your dreams. Don't quit!" Even when the dream seems "preposterous", it is still real to a *Keeper of Dreams*. A person is never too young or too old to have a dream.

A. How can you be a Keeper of Dreams?

1. Write down your dream or draw a picture of it.
2. List the steps you need to take to make your dream come true.
3. Begin to work on them now!
4. If you would like to share your dream with others, it might be fun to act it out. Can others guess what it is?

B. Dreams can help you discover your own talents and abilities. They can help you understand yourself, your goals, what makes you happy. You might be the rare person who knows what he or she wants to do from an an early age – or your dreams might change as you grow older. *The world needs the special contributions only you can make!*

III. **DREAM HELPERS encourage a Keeper of Dreams to keep trying, to keep believing in the dream.** Some people might make fun of a *Keeper of Dreams* or say the dream is silly or impossible. Some people might try to force their own dreams on a Keeper of Dreams. However, Dream Helpers respect *Keepers of Dreams* and help make their dreams come true.

A. How can you find a Dream Helper?

1. Look for someone you trust: a parent, relative, teacher, pastor, etc.
2. Talk to that person about your dream.
3. Ask that person to help you.

B. How can you be a Dream Helper?

1. Listen to others tell about their dreams.
2. Respect them ... and don't make fun of their dreams.
3. Talk to them and ask how you can help.
4. Encourage them – especially when they are discouraged!
5. Your interest in them and their dream is the best help you can give them.

Not everyone has a Dream Helper. As you will discover on the following pages, some *Keepers of Dreams* had to be extra strong because no one else could understand their goal. Fortunately for us, they didn't give up!

"The only people who never fail are those who never try."
ILKA CHASE

IV. **DREAMS COME TRUE!** Think about all the wonderful things we have received from *Keepers of Dreams*: art, music, books, medicine, electricity, telephones, cars, bridges, airplanes ... WOW!

A. Who are the Keepers of Dreams?

1. Can you name something that came from someone's dream ... and the Keeper of Dreams who did it?

2. Do you know any Keepers of Dreams? How do you know about them? Did they tell you, or did you see them working hard to make their dream come true?

B. **REMEMBER:** A Keeper of Dreams holds on to his or her dream and tries to make the world a better place. Usually the dream we have tells something about who we are and what's important to us!

"Whatever you can do or dream you can begin it.
Boldness has genius, power, and magic in it.
Begin it now." **GOETHE**

FAMOUS KEEPERS OF DREAMS

Here are just a few of the many thousands of *Keeper of Dreams* who have worked hard to have their dreams come true. You can see even from this short list how many different and wonderful dreams there have been.

"There is no failure except in no longer trying. There is no defeat except from within." ELBERT GREEN HUBBARD

One 10-year-old girl named SAMANTHA SMITH wrote a letter to the soviet premier, Yuri Andropov, telling him of her hope for our two countries to live together in peace. Several months later she and her parents received a note inviting them to visit the Soviet Union. At this time there was great tension between our nations. Yet, during her visit Samantha captured the hearts of children and adults wherever she went and helped ease tension between our two countries.

One of our greatest presidents, ABRAHAM LINCOLN, failed twice in business, had a nervous breakdown, and was defeated in seven elections before he became President. Because he believed that "all men are created equal" he fought to put an end to slavery. Even though he died over 100 years ago, his dream for freedom for all inspires and encourages people everywhere.

The Cherokee Indian SEQUOYAH had never seen written words before he watched a white man read a message on a "talking leaf" (piece of paper). When he went home, SEQUOYAH took bark and charcoal and begin to draw pictures for the sounds of Cherokee words. People laughed at him. His wife got mad and threw all his work into the fire. But he started over again. After many years of work a special tribal council (meeting) was held for Sequoyah. He was kept outside by guards. Inside, the chief gave his 10-year-old daughter, Ah-yoka, a message to write. When Sequoyah was brought in, he was able to read what she had written. The people were amazed! Everyone wanted to learn to read, and Sequoyah taught them how. By 1828 the Cherokee nation had printed books, newspapers, magazines, and a Bible ... all because one man followed the dream of giving his people a written language. He was very short of stature and lame, but the big redwood trees are named sequoia for him.

After being in school only 3 months, THOMAS EDISON was sent home because his teacher thought he was too stupid to try to teach. Tom's mother disagreed. She believed her son was intelligent and creative, so she taught him at home. Tom wanted to discover new things. He became one of the great inventors of all time. One of his inventions took months of hard work and thousands of experiments – but finally he succeeded in inventing the electric light bulb. Then he worked creating an entire electrical system. Imagine our world today if Thomas Edison hadn't worked hard for his dreams to come true!

As JENNY BUTCHART looked out at the huge, ugly, gouged-out rock quarry, she dreamed of creating a beautiful garden. And, so, in 1904 she began by planting some sweet peas and roses. Over the years, tons of soil were brought in, thousands of shrubs and flowers were planted, pathways and bridges were built. Statues, waterfalls, and dancing fountains were added. Today, people from all over the world travel to Victoria, Canada to see a "North American Paradise" – the BUTCHART GARDENS.

If Theodor Seuss Geisel (DR. SEUSS) had quit after 23 rejections, no one would have been able to read his book AND TO THINK I SAW IT ON MULBERRY STREET! This story was turned down by 23 editors. But Dr. Seuss tried once again, and it was published, along with many, many other wonderful stories. So those of you who love to write, don't get discouraged. Hold onto your dreams – keep sending out your stories, keep writing ... and remember Dr. Seuss.

It took much more than wishing upon a star for the dreams of WALT DISNEY to come true. He grew up in a very poor family, and his father didn't want him to have a career in art. Walt worked hard and saved his money so he could go to art school. His first job as a artist lasted only six weeks. Then he got a job where he learned animation - how to make drawings that appear to move when photographed. (Over 1400 drawings are needed for a one-minute cartoon!) Walt changed jobs– succeeding and failing many times. Finally, Mickey Mouse was created, and Walt was on the road to success with even bigger dreams! He created full-length cartoon movies and three wonderful dream parks. Disneyland, DisneyWorld, and Epcot Center. When asked if his success surprised him, Walt replied, "Why, no. I believed in it." And because he did, his dreams live on today.

Born in Serbia (a part of Yugoslavia) in 1910, Ganxhe Agnes Bojaxhiu had parents who always shared what they had with the poor. Guests were at their table every day. When Agnes once asked who they were, her mother said, "Some are relatives, but all of them are our people." When she grew up Agnes knew she wanted to be a missionary and become a nun. In 1928 she traveled to Ireland, joining the Order of Loreto nuns and changing her name to **MOTHER TERESA** of the Child Jesus. Today, in India, **MOTHER TERESA** is living out her dream of helping starving, homeless people, the sick and dying of all ages. She has shown how despair can be turned into hope, and if hope fails, then there will always be love. Of course, money has been important to help the poor be fed, clothed, and cared for. But MOTHER TERESA has said, "Money is not enough; they need your hearts to love them. So spread love everywhere you go: first of all in your own home."

"I have a dream," said DR. MARTIN LUTHER KING, JR. "It is a dream deeply rooted in the American dream that one day this nation will rise up and live out the true meaning of its creed – 'We hold these truths to be self evident, that all men are created equal.' " When Dr. King was growing up in the South, black and white people were kept separate. Each had their own schools, restaurants, parks, even drinking fountains. This was called segregation. Dr. King knew this wasn't right. He tried to make changes for his people. He wanted the changes to be brought about peacefully. He met with President John F. Kennedy in 1962 and urged him to pass a bill that would end segregation. The Civil Rights Act of 1964 made segregation illegal. Dr King's dream was for the fair treatment of everyone and for the brotherhood of all people.

I wish I had enough room to include thousands more "Keepers of Dreams." Perhaps someday your name could be on a list like this. Do you have a dream?

Remember: *"Your Dreams can come true. It's up to you."*

ALEXANDRA QUACKENDIVER

About the Author

Mary Alice Baumgardner was born and spent her early childhood in Hagerstown, Maryland, where she and her family visited City Park. She loved to feed the ducks on the lake and listen to the beautiful music at outdoor concerts. Mary Alice graduated from Gettysburg College and has taught elementary school, art, and high school French. She continued her studies in art most recently in Florence, Italy. She is a member of the Society of Children's Book Writers and Illustrators. Mary Alice lives in Waynesboro, Pennsylvania, with her husband, Allen, and sons, Matthew, Mark, and Michael.

For over 20 years Mary Alice has written and illustrated children's stories. ALEXANDRA– KEEPER OF DREAMS is her first published work.